Knowing Acts

Engage in Healing

By Heidi Love

Art by Linden O'Ryan

Foreword by Anne Hallward, MD

Laughing AT THE SKY

LAUGHING AT THE SKY BOOKS | FIRST EDITION | MAINE | 2021

Foreword

The work of healing from trauma requires tremendous courage. It means finding safe ways to revisit what was unbearable through the eyes and heart of self compassion, until what was unbearable becomes bearable and surrounded by tenderness. Building a compassionate relationship with yourself can be difficult. This book is here to help.

Heidi Love has used her own struggle and her own deep work to heal, and turned it into a gift. Born of her intimate knowledge and experience with overwhelming painful feelings, this guide was created to be full of so many choices and resources for when the going gets rough. I see this book as a kind of touchstone, a source of deep grounding and clarity about who you are, what really matters to you, and where you can turn for strength when you need it most.

Each of the ACTS that Heidi offers in this book are invitations to courage, to clarity, and to calm. They help build a connection inside that will support and strengthen you to do the work of healing in your own therapy. This book is best used as a companion during the process of therapy, to help hold you through what can sometimes feel like a long week between sessions. Choosing to go toward your most painful memories may be the bravest gift you ever give yourself. You won't be walking this path alone. Knowing Acts can be your companion and guide.

— Anne Hallward MD

Founder and Executive Director, Safe Space Radio

Assistant Clinical Professor of Psychiatry,
Tufts University Medical School

"THE WOUND IS THE PLACE
WHERE THE LIGHT ENTERS YOU"

— RUMI

OH WOMAN OF SORROW

Dedication

We all carry stories. Some of our stories raise us up; others weigh us down. The creators of this book stand with all of the strong and emerging voices, those who have transcended their stories and emerged stronger, and those who are suffering from overwhelming emotions. You are not alone. We dedicate this book to YOU & to our collective tribe of transcendence. May we rise together, stronger—with love.

To Nico whose love, laughter, wisdom, and encouragement lift me up and allow me to soar. With you everything seems possible. To Dennis, for journeying through life with me, sitting on the edge of the world, feet hanging over.

— Heidi

To Brennen, who walked with me through my journey from here and from the beyond. And to art for its healing process of exploration and transformation. In gratitude and love.

— Linden

Engage in Healing

Knowing Acts is a customizable workbook for a personal journey of healing. It offers engaging ways to create an automatic response or PRACTICE for those suffering from overwhelming sadness, grief, despair, anger, numbness or loss, and experiencing PTSD, suicidal thoughts, trauma, or hardship.

Knowing Acts offers thirty easy, pleasant-to-do exercises or ACTS with music, art, mindfulness, podcasts, power clothes, haiku, and more. There are also selections of brave books, websites, and free resources.

When I was eleven I survived violent crime and my mother's condemnation that I was "ruined for life." As an adult I suffered from PTSD. At times my self-esteem would plummet and I wasn't in a place to make healthy decisions. With the support of therapists I created a book that guided me through an automatic response or PRACTICE. This helped keep me feeling safer by avoiding the worst of downward emotional spirals and stabilizing my mood enough to seek help. Eventually I learned where my suffering was coming from and how to find peace.

Anyone can easily start Knowing Acts on their own; however, it is best when ultimately used with a therapist. By itself it is not a magical, long-term solution, but having a PRACTICE can be an effective way to defuse overwhelming emotions and reduce suffering.

The first ACT is to turn the page and start.

With love,

One Step – ACT

This book is a result of my sailing journey to French Polynesia, a lifelong dream that kept me going after violent crime at age eleven *(pages 76, 94)*. It ultimately saved me and is here for your personal journey of healing. Everyone's trauma or hardship experiences, practices, and recoveries are different. You can start with any ACT that appeals to you.

A list of ACTS is on page 10, followed by over 30 ACTS on pages 12 to 75. Left-hand pages give examples, while right-hand pages have spaces for you to complete.

Detailed instructions begin on page 78. There are numerous accounts of personal experiences here that supported my healing.

Some readers start by creating a playlist *(page 15);* others prefer breathing exercises *(page 19)*, visualizing peaceful places *(page 35)*, art *(page 37)*, dance *(page 49)*, or haiku *(page 57)*. Once you're familiar with the exercises you can return to the PACT *(page 9)*, sign it, and continue your healing journey by creating your own PRACTICE *(page 11)*.

BRIGHT SHADES OF MAGIC

THE JOURNEY OF A THOUSAND MILES
STARTS WITH ONE STEP

— Lao-Tzu

COMMITMENT IS AN ACT,
NOT A WORD.

— Jean Paul Sartre

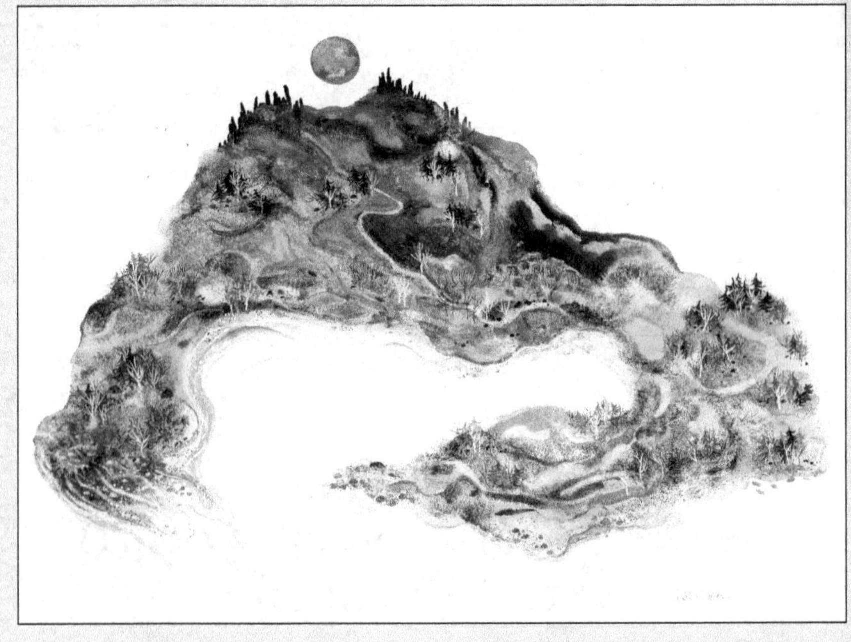

GLIMMERING FROM ABOVE

The Pact

I ______________________________

(sign your name)

will learn new ways to address

overwhelming sadness, anger, & feelings

of loss or despair, and grab this book

TO ACT

if I start to spiral down.

SEE PAGE 78

Love's Practice

These are ACTS I take if I'm overwhelmed. If you are just starting this workbook, choose any ACT below that appeals to you.

*My Practice**

* COMPLETE THIS PAGE AFTER YOU'VE TRIED SEVERAL ACTS. SEE PAGE 79

*Sample Safety Plan**

- If I'm in immediate danger, I will **call 911** or my local police, and go to my safe place.

- If I need to talk to a sexual assault hotline, I will call the **RAINN Helpline at 800-656-HOPE (4673)**. There are also state and local resources. My state and local resources are **Maine Coalition Against Sexual Assault (MECASA)** and **Sexual Assault Response Services of Southern Maine (SARSSM) at 800-871-7741.**

- If I'm in crisis, I will call the **National Suicide Prevention hotline at 800-273-TALK (8255)**.

- If I am experiencing domestic violence, I will call the **National Domestic Violence Hotline at 1-800-799-SAFE (7233).**

- I will talk to anyone in my support group *(page 42)* and tell them: *"I am not in a good place, please help. My location is ..."*

* THERE ARE MANY WAYS WE CAN REDUCE THE RISKS OF VIOLENCE. CHECK OUT LOVE'S RESOURCES PAGE 62

SUNLIT WISDOM

My Safety Plan

You Are Not Alone

SEE PAGE 79

Love's Playlist 1
*Songs of Power & Joy**

- *Breathe* — Anna Nalick
- *Fuckin' Perfect* — Pink
- *Rise Up* — Andra Day
- *Stand by Me* — Tracy Chapman
- *Keep Your Head Up* — Ben Howard
- *Phenomenal Woman* — Ruthie Foster
- *Reach* — Gloria Estefan
- *Better Days* — Ant Clemons and Justin Timberlake
- *Firework* — Katy Perry
- *I Believe I Can Fly* — Etta James
- *The Sound of Sunshine* — Michael Franti
- *You Can Get It If You Really Want* — Jimmy Cliff
- *Three Little Birds* — Bob Marley and the Wailers
- *True Colors* — Cyndi Lauper
- *Here Comes the Sun* — The Beatles
- *What a Wonderful World* — Louis Armstrong
- *Little Bird* — Annie Lennox
- *Ooh Ooh Child* — MILC
- *Alive* — Sia
- *Lovely Day* — Bill Withers
- *Gonna Fly Now* — Bill Conti
- *Still I Rise* — Maya Angelou, Caged Bird Songs
- *Girl on Fire* — Alicia Keys
- *Somewhere Over the Rainbow* — Israel Kamakawiwo'ole

* AVAILABLE ON SPOTIFY. VISIT HEIDILOVEAUTHOR.COM/PLAYLIST FOR A LINK TO THIS PLAYLIST.

MUSIC WAS MY REFUGE

— *Maya Angelou*

*My Playlist**

Create your own playlists filled with songs that lift you up. Start below by listing one song.

___

___

___

___

___

___

___

___

___

___

___

___

___

* LISTEN TO LOVE'S PLAYLISTS BY VISITING HEIDILOVEAUTHOR.COM/PLAYLIST. DISCOVER SONGS FROM OTHER READERS, AND SHARE YOURS ON SPOTIFY WITH THE NAME "KNOWING ACTS YOUR NAME" AND ADD THE LINK, OR SONG NAMES, AT THE BOTTOM OF THE HEIDILOVEAUTHOR.COM/ PLAYLIST WEBSITE. LIKES ARE ALWAYS APPRECIATED. ♥

SEE PAGE 79

ESSENTIAL OILS

BREATHE IN ROSE

CALM WITH ORANGE

BE PRESENT WITH GRAPEFRUIT

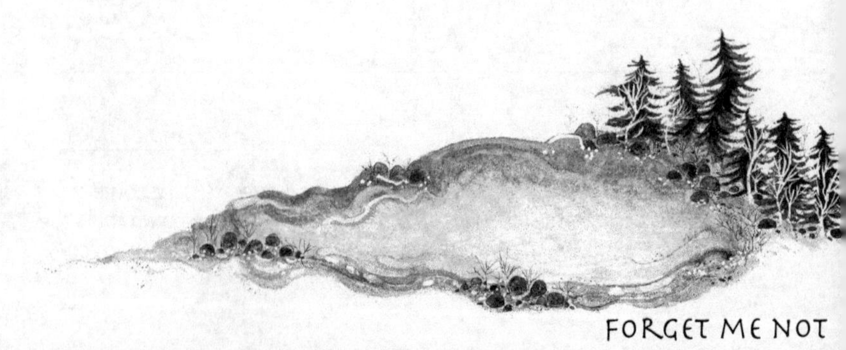

MY FRAGRANCES

SEE PAGE 80

Love's Breathing Spaces & Mantra

NO ONE CAN FIND THE REWIND BUTTON,
GIRL, SO CRADLE YOUR HEAD IN YOUR
HANDS AND BREATHE, JUST BREATHE
OH, BREATHE, JUST BREATHE.

— Song by Anna Nalick

First breathe:

INHALE — Close my mouth and inhale deeply through my nose while counting to five. Feel my abdomen expand.

HOLD — At the top of my breath, count to five as I hold my breath.

EXHALE — Exhale the fullness of my breath through my mouth while counting to ten.

REPEAT

Then Speak — Repeat this Mantra:

Breathing in, I breathe in calm
Breathing out, I release stress

Breathing in, I feel present
Breathing out, I feel connected to my body

Breathing in, I breathe in focus
Breathing out, I feel calm

My Precious Breath

This space is for quick, one-minute grounding ACTS. Write your own mantras here. Page 38 has a place for more lengthy meditations.

SEE PAGES 81, 84

Love's Presence

Trauma distorts time and can make us feel in danger when we may not be. Ground yourself in the present. Take a deep breath, stretch, and gently release emotions.

Ask:

- What day is it?
- What year is it?
- Where am I?
- Who am I with now?

Do:

- Name five things I see around myself now.
- Name four things I feel with my hands.
- Name three things I hear.
- Name two things I smell.
- Name one thing I taste.

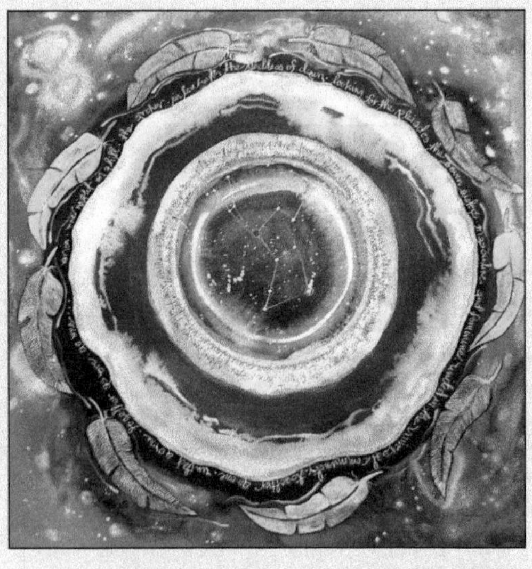

DANCING IN THE HEAVENS

Be Present

Use the space below to write your own grounding ACTS or simply answer the questions to the left.

Love's Inspiring Quotes

"Fear, to a great extent, is born of a story we tell ourselves, and so I chose to tell myself a different story from the one women are told. I decided I was safe. I was strong. I was brave. Nothing could vanquish me."

— Cheryl Straye

"Have enough courage to trust love one more time and always one more time." — Maya Angelo

"Being powerful is a state of mind." — Naide P. Obiang

"I say I am stronger than fear. — Malala Yousafza

"Fears are not always conquered; some can't be. Maybe the best we can hope for is to stand side by side with them instead of letting them crush you .... I made the effort in spite of my terror."

— Michelle Bowdler

"At the moment of action, you don't see [courage] as a courageous act. Courage is the most hidden thing for your eye or mind until after it's done."

— Unita Blackwell

"There is the risk you cannot afford to take and there is the risk you cannot afford not to take." — Peter Drucker

"You are braver than you believe, stronger than you seem, and smarter than you think." — A. A. Milne

"You have only one life—live it!" — Ann Daniels

"You are not alone. We see you, we hear you ... we're here too."

— Me Too

My Quotes

Photos I Love

More Photos

PASTE PHOTOS, SKETCH, OR MAKE LISTS OF IMAGES YOU LOVE. *SEE PAGE 81*

Love's Calming Thoughts

Moments that calm me:

1. Gramma Katie making homemade chicken soup: the chicken in her fingers, her flowered apron, the aroma, the warm buttery taste, and her hugs.
2. My son's contagious smile, how his face gets red and his eyes sparkle, his laugh, holding my photo of him in his red shirt.
3. The Rachel Carson Marsh, a beautiful preserve where I can breathe in healing fragrances of the sea and salt; hear the cry of the loon; feel the wind on my face; and feel whole.
4. Happy dogs, especially a dachshund named Heidi and a Dalmatian named Tasha. Imagine them running in the marsh.
5. The sounds when ocean waves crash over pebbles and then recede; it's as if the pebbles are applauding the magnificent waves.
6. Homemade iced tea; stirring it with a wooden spoon and tasting it while it is still warm; feeling the warmth with both hands on the green pot; tasting the slight sweetness; imagining the growing of the tea plants and sugar cane; the sun and rain that supported their growth; the rich earth that nurtured the seed; the clouds that influenced the wind that blows the sugar cane.
7. Skiing on snowy mountains; making large slow turns on a bluebird day, the sun shining on my face, reflecting off the snow; the powder spraying a light magical plume behind me.
8. Wearing my red Rocky shirt.
9. My friends singing Bob Marley's *One Love*.

My Calming Thoughts

Love's Good Traits

- I am a loving mom
- I am a kind and caring wife
- I am a compassionate sister
- I am a great sailor
- I bring joy to friends
- I help people in need
- I am a board member, activist, & volunteer
- I am truthful
- I have compassion
- I have raised considerable funds for causes
- I have made numerous friends who love me
- I have written two books
- I have sailed over 12,000 miles
- I survived trauma *& am rising above it!*

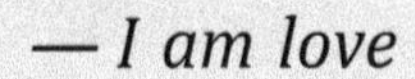

— I am love

These are traits people have expressed to me. When I am triggered it can be very difficult to believe any of them. By writing them here I can begin to remember parts of me that I forget in crises.

My Good Traits

— I am who I am

— I am love

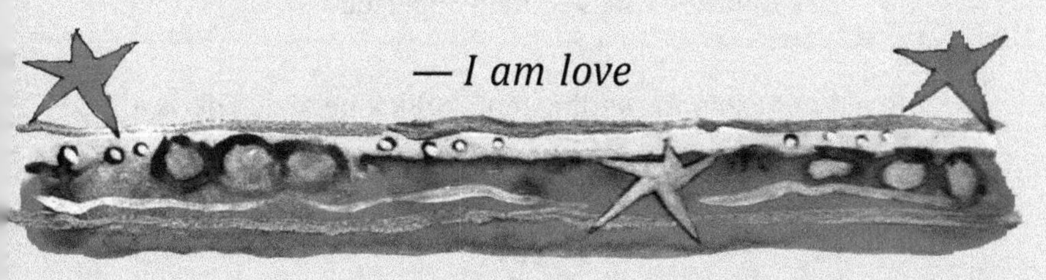

SEE PAGE 82

Love's Nourishment

1. Full glass of water (drink slowly)
2. PowerBar
3. Ice tea
4. Protein
    - Hard-boiled egg
    - Almond butter on grain cracker
    - Protein shake*
5. Chocolate pieces

    (eat slowly and savor;
    be present with each bite)

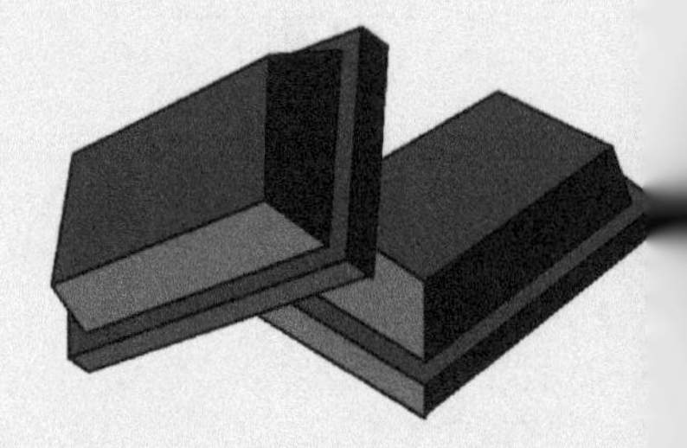

*** Recipe for Hannah's Banana Protein Shake**

In a blender add:

- 1 frozen banana
- 1 cup or several leaves of kale (preferably Tuscan kale); remove the thick part of the stalk
- ¼ cup Greek yogurt
- ½ cup almond milk
- *(optional)* ¼ cup of wild Maine blueberries
- *(optional)* 1 scoop of protein powder i.e Amazing Grass Protein Superfood

Blend until smooth, adding more milk if needed. This is a 100-calorie treat, high in protein, vitamins, and calcium.

Enjoy!

My Nourishment

Love's Inspirations

I derive inspiration from the sea and her creatures. I like to imagine swimming with whales.

> *"Gamble everything for love, if you are a true human being. If not, leave this gathering. Half-heartedness doesn't reach into majesty. You set out to find God, but then you keep stopping for long periods at mean-spirited roadhouses. Don't wait any longer. Dive in the ocean, leave, and let the sea be you."*
>
> — *Rumi*

My Inspiration

Add spiritual or religious prayers or quotes, personal art or poetry that inspires you.

EVENING SONG

SEE PAGE 83

Love's Place of Beauty

PURLING WATER FOR MY SOUL

The Rachel Carson Marsh

Breathe deep and imagine the fragrances of a fresh, briny sea. Listen to crying loons and the sounds of waves flowing and receding. Feel the wind on your face and the sun on your cheeks. Taste salt on your lips. Close your eyes and bring the marsh to your heart.

My Places of Beauty & Peace

SEE PAGE 84

Love's Puzzles, Coloring, Games & other Distractions

Try an online or smartphone jigsaw puzzle, e.g., National Geographic Jigsaw Puzzle, or do mindful coloring:

- *Color Me Calm* — Lacy Mucklow and Angela Porter
- *The Mindfulness Coloring Book* — Emma Farrarons
- *The One and Only Coloring Book for Adults* — Phoenix Yard Books
- *Secret Garden: An Inky Treasure Hunt and Coloring Book for Adults* — Johanna Basford

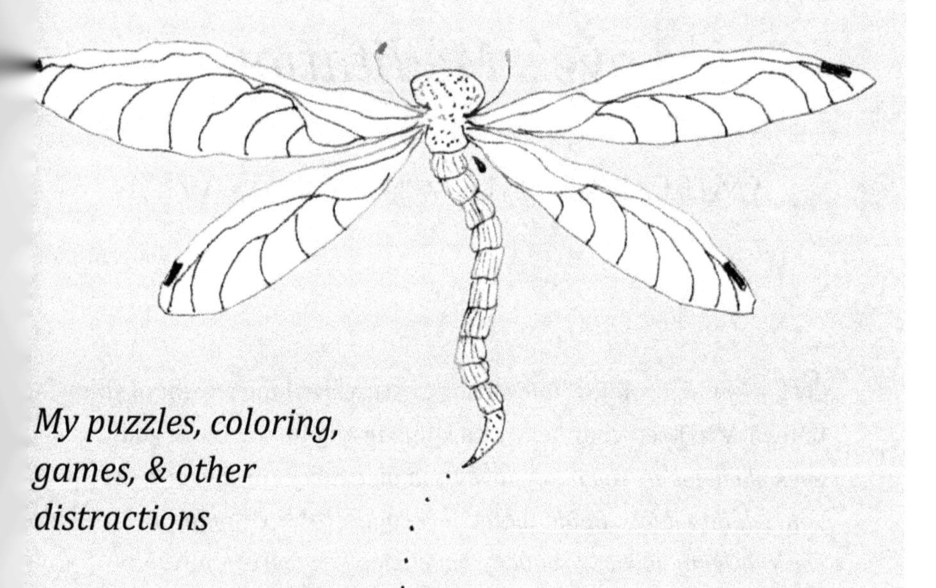

My puzzles, coloring, games, & other distractions

color me

Love's Meditation

SMILE, BREATHE, AND GO SLOWLY.

— *Thich Nhất Hanh*

Sit — Find a comfortable sitting posture. Feel the weight of your body. Try to keep your head and spine in alignment. Close your eyes. *Remember: You don't have to sit on a fancy cushion or twist yourself into knots. Being seated in a comfortable straight-backed chair or lying down are equally beneficial. Just feel comfortable and supported.*

Breathe — Try to let go of your thoughts and focus on your breath. Breathe in through your nose. Breathe out through your nose. Put your hands on your belly to help yourself breathe all the way in. Expand on the inhale, contract on the exhale. *Remember: thoughts will interfere—that's okay. Once you find yourself "thinking," come back to your breath. Don't judge, just come back to your breath. The ACT of showing up and trying is perfect.*

In time, expand — Expand your awareness of breathing within your body. Move attention outward from your stomach and lungs. Feel your body from the crown of your head to your toes. Feel your skin and the air that caresses your body. Continue your breathing for several minutes until you feel ready to move on.

Return — Allow your eyes to open. Slowly move out of your meditation. Smile.

My Meditation

List your own meditation steps or applications e.g. *Headspace, Aura*, or *Calm*.

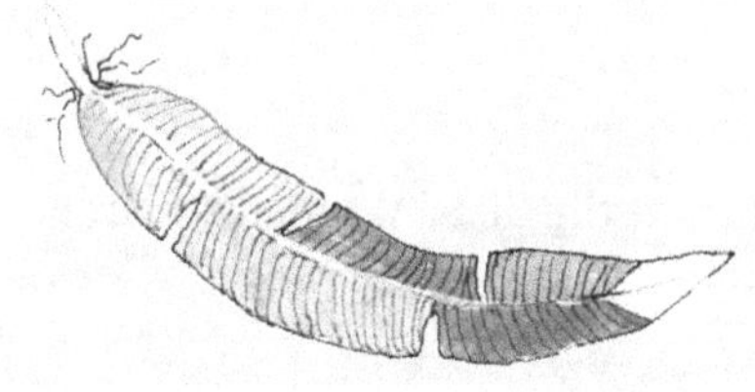

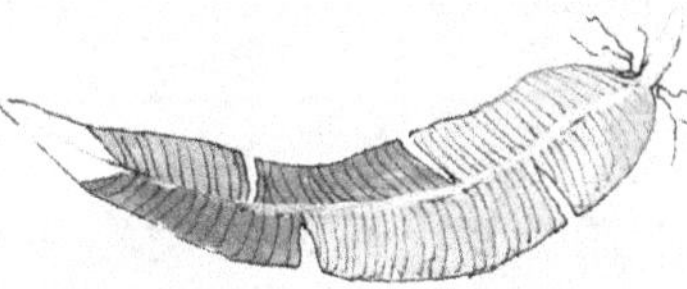

SEE PAGE 84

Love's Power Clothes & Totems

Put on your red Rocky "Love Wins" shirt.
Hold your small pebble & clay turtle close to your heart.

I wore my Rocky "Love Wins" shirt at the 2017 Women's March.

My Power Clothes & Totems

Looking better, wearing your favorite "power" clothes, or simply washing your face can make you feel better. Holding a power item can also help. List ways you can look or feel stronger.

SEE PAGE 85

Love's Friends, Contacts, & Support

Support Friends:

- Dennis **207 - [illegible] - [illegible]**
- Judy **207 - [illegible] - [illegible]**
- Susan **603 - [illegible] - [illegible]**
- Janet **207 - [illegible] - [illegible]**

Professional Support:

- My Therapist **207 - [illegible] - [illegible]**
- MECASA/SARSSM in Maine
  1 - 800 - 871 - 7741
- RAINN National Helpline
  1 - 800 - 656 - 4673
- National Suicide Prevention Hotline
  1 - 800 - 273 - 8255
- National Domestic Violence Hotline
  1 - 800 - 799 - SAFE (7233)

My Friends & Support

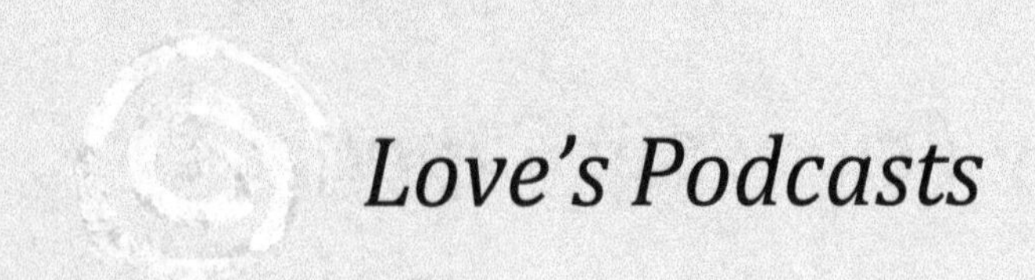

Love's Podcasts

Safe Space Radio:
"What is the story that you're keeping quietly in your own heart? How would it be ... if you let yourself imagine that this story could be one of the greatest gifts you have to offer ... an act of courage, generosity, and cultural leadership."

— Dr. Anne Hallward

Unbroken: Healing Through Storytelling:
"We are not defined by what knocks us down; we are defined by how we get back up."

— Madeleine Black

Dear Sugar:
"You will learn a lot about yourselves if you stretch in the direction of goodness, of bigness, of kindness, of forgiveness, of emotional bravery. Be a warrior for love."

— Cheryl Strayed

Super Soul Conversations
"Breathe. Let go. And remind yourself that this very moment is the only one you know you have for sure."

— Oprah Winfrey

And More:

- *10% Happier* — Dan Harris
- *Unlocking Us* — Brené Brown
- *Mindful Recovery* — Robert Cox
- *Call Your Girlfriend* — Friedman & Sow

My Podcasts

Love's Exercises

Stretch — Yoga — Run — Laugh
Walk among the pines

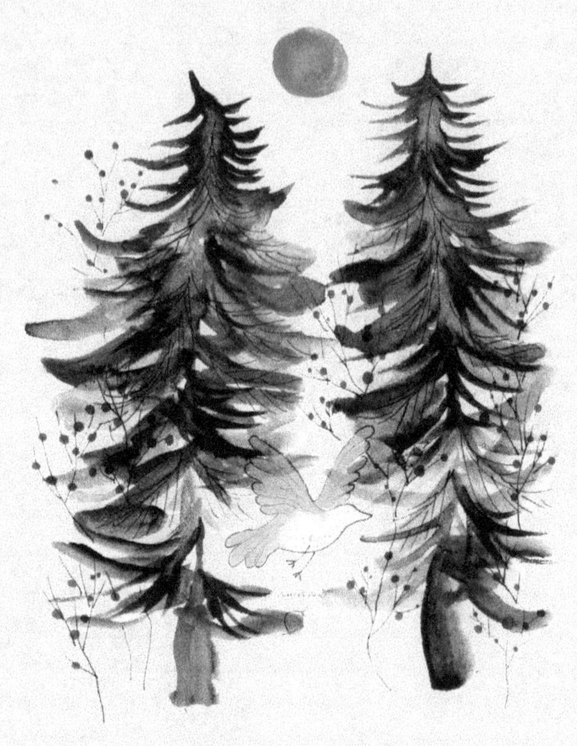

THE BREATH OF THE PINES

I FEEL THE BREATH OF THE PINES, THE SOUL OF THE TREES, AS A WALK CHANGES THE AIR IN MY LUNGS, THE LIFT IN MY STEP, AND THE NOTES IN MY SOUL.

— Linden O'Ryan

*My Exercises**

* TRY TO BE SPECIFIC. IF YOU DO YOGA, WHAT IS YOUR FAVORITE STRETCH? IF YOU RUN OR WALK, WHERE CAN YOU EASILY DO THAT? IF YOU CANNOT FULLY EXERCISE, INCLUDE WHATEVER MOVES YOU.

SEE PAGE 86

Love's Dances

"Laughter, song, and dance create emotional and spiritual connection; they remind us of the one thing that truly matters when we are searching for comfort, celebration, inspiration, or healing. We are not alone."

—Brené Brown

*My Dances**

* DESCRIBE HOW YOU MIGHT DANCE TO RELEASE EMOTIONS, OR ADD SONGS HERE THAT MOVE YOU IN POSITIVE WAYS.

SEE PAGE 87

Love's Playlist 2
*Songs to Calm & Soothe**

Instrumental

- *Song for Humanity* — Peter Kater, R. Carlos Nakai
- *Are You Going with Me* — Pat Metheny
- *Nara* — E.S. Posthumus
- *Paint My Heart Red* — by Keith Jarrett
- *Cutting Through the Ocean of Ego* — Nawang Khechog
- *Positive Mind Jazz* — Cafe Music BGM
- *Moonlight Sonata, Piano Sonata No. 14* — Ludwig van Beethoven

International

- *Return to Innocence* — Enigma
- *Electra* — Airstream
- *Sense* — Digitonal
- *Little Rays* — Echaskech
- *Under the Glow* — Laki Mera
- *Baro* — Habib Koité Bamada

*Nature Playlists**

- *Forest Nature Sounds* — Birds
- *Meditate to the Sounds of Nature*
- *Nature Meditation: Earth*

WEEPING MOONLIGHT

* AVAILABLE ON SPOTIFY. VISIT HEIDILOVEAUTHOR.COM/PLAYLIST FOR A FREE LINK.

My Playlist 2
*Calming Music & Nature Sounds**

* CONSIDER SHARING YOUR PLAY LIST ON SPOTIFY. VISIT HEIDILOVEAUTHOR.COM/PLAYLIST.

SEE PAGES 79, 87

Love's Examples of Courage

Transcending Life's Challenges

Read *LaughingAtTheSky.org*

People Who Inspire Me

Dr. Anne Hallward says, "Courage is contagious."
Find people who have transcended life's challenges.

FACING PAGE, WOMEN OF COURAGE FROM LAUGHINGATTHESKY.ORG.

TOP: LINDA(KRETZ) KRETZLER. LEFT TO RIGHT: HIBO WARDERE, CECILIA ARAGON, AND ANN DANIELS

SEE PAGE 87

Love's Favorite Poetry

"Life has broken me into a million shards. But like ocean salt on a coastline, I am still so glorious in my fragmentation."

A Sunday on the Island of Woman — Amanda Gorman

"Just be here with me. Signed: The moon. The stars ... The skyline. The earth beneath your feet. Your passion project. The shade of a giant tree. This moment, right here, now. Your bones. Your belly laugh. Your breath. Your breath. Your breath."

— Morgan Day Cecil

Now we are leaving
The butterflies can make love
To their hearts' desire

A Haiku — Kobayashi Issa

— Linden O'Ryan

My Poetry
Copy it, Write it, Slam it!

Janet's Haiku

Creating 5 - 7 - 5 Patterns to Calm

Think about haiku
Calm the mind slowly until
Gently sleep returns.

Strong winds of change free
Compassionate energy
Breathing love on all.

Morphing grief pulsing
Energy, relief, to light
The world around us.

Take a breath to pause
Feel opportunity glow
Radiating joy.

Rejuvenated
Grace humbled by all that is
Within and without.

— Janet Clemons

REVIVIFY

*My Haiku**

____

____

____

____

____

____

____

____

____

** READ MORE HAIKU'S AND CONSIDER SHARING YOURS BY VISITING HEIDILOVEAUTHOR.COM/HAIKU*

SEE PAGE 88

Love's Gratitude

"What you focus on expands" — Esther Jno-Charles

"I will focus on Love" — Heidi Love

Repeat:

1. I am grateful for my son, Nico
2. I am grateful for my husband, Dennis
3. I am grateful for his son, Ethan
4. I am grateful for his daughter, Hannah
5. I am grateful for my eyes and reading this book
6. I am grateful for being warm
7. I am grateful for extended family and friends

Name:

Five things I can be grateful for in this moment:

1. ______________________________

2. ______________________________

3. ______________________________

4. ______________________________

5. ______________________________

My Gratitude

List seven things you are always grateful for at the top. Use the bottom circles to find momentary gratitude around you.

1. ______________________________

2. ______________________________

3. ______________________________

4. ______________________________

5. ______________________________

6. ______________________________

7. ______________________________

The numbers below are here to remind you to name things you are grateful for in any given moment.

FOLLOWING HEART

SEE PAGE 89

Love's Brave Books

Mindfulness

- *Peace is Every Step* — Thich Nhat Hanh
- *10% Happier* — Dan Harris
- *You Belong: A Call for Connection* — Sebene Selassie
- *Real Happiness: The Power of Meditation* — Sharon Salzberg

Poetry

- *The Essential Rumi* — Jalal al-Din Rumi
- *Maya Angelou: Poems* — Maya Angelou

Sexual Assault and Other Trauma

- *The Courage to Heal* — Laura Davis
- *The Courage to Heal Workbook* — Ellen Bass, Laura Davis
- *Is Rape a Crime? A Memoir, an Investigation, and a Manifesto* — Michelle Bowdler
- *The PTSD Workbook* — Mary Beth Williams, Soili Poijula
- *Healing Steps* — Sharyn Higdon Jones
- *My Grandmother's Hands* — Resmaa Menakem

Self Help

- *If the Buddha Got Stuck* — Charlotte Kasl
- *Finding Joy: 101 ways to free your spirit and dance with life* — Charlotte Davis Kasl, Lenore Davis
- *When Things Fall Apart* — Pema Chödrön
- *A Year of Resilience: 52 Ideas to be More Resilient and Stay Afloat Throughout the Year* — Maureen Orey
- *Burnout: The Secret to Unlocking the Stress Cycle* — Emily Nagoski, Amelia Nagoski

Inspiration

- *The Little Book of Inner Peace* — Dalai Lama
- *Shortcuts to Inner Peace* — Ashley Davis Bush
- *What I Know For Sure* — Oprah Winfrey
- *Brave Enough* — Cheryl Strayed
- *The Book of Joy* — Dalai Lama, Desmond Tutu
- *In Love with the World* — Yongey Mingyur Rinpoche

My Brave Books

Love's Online Resources

Inspiration

- HeidiLoveAuthor.com
  A community of strong & emerging voices
- LaughingAtTheSky.org
  Stories of courage and rising above challenges to live our dreams
- LindenORyan.com
  The artist behind Knowing Acts

Trauma

- PsychologyToday.com/us/therapists
  A list of therapists and their backgrounds across the United States and beyond; you can search by zip code
- SafeSpaceRadio.com
  Stories that inspire courageous conversations, reduce stigma, shame, and isolation, and foster compassion and public health
- MeTooMvmt.org
  Supporting survivor healing and disrupting rape culture
- DoraMcQuaid.com
  One woman's voice; a resource for survivors
- NSVRC.org
  National Sexual Violence Resource Center
- RAINN.org
  Rape, Abuse & Incest National Network
  Resources, live chat & helpline
- IamWomankind.org
  Resources and helplines for rising above violence

Mindfulness

- ThichNhatHanhFoundation.org
  Mindfulness practices
- UCLAHealth.org/marc
  Free guided meditation Mindful.org — Healthy mind, healthy life
- FreeMindfulness.org
  Free mindfulness resource

My Online Resources

*Love's Rituals**

There are many rituals that calm us. These are a few of mine.

- *Start your tea ritual*

    1. Put the teakettle on
    2. Make a cup of Clarity and Calm Tea*
    3. Breathe in the aroma and let it swirl through you
    4. Feel the warmth of Gramma Katie's teacup
    5. Remember Katie's comfort
    6. Slowly sip the tea
    7. Let the warmth fill you

- *Water your plants and pay attention to their growth.*

- *Take a warm bath and let the water soothe you.*

** THE REPUBLIC OF TEA*

My Rituals

SEE PAGE 89

Free-form Creativity

Use this space for anything that might
lift you up from wherever you might be.

Free-form Creativity

Use this space to keep rising.

Love's Phone

I use the Note section on my phone to hold my Action Plan, important phone and text information, reminders of my Spotify playlists, and special photo folders I have created. I'm rarely without my phone, so this information is near whenever I need it.

1. **My PRACTICE** *(page 10)*
2. **Important phone and text numbers** *(page 42)*
3. **Spotify playlists** *(pages 14, 50)*
4. **A special photo file** *(page 24)*
5. **My podcasts** *(page 44)*

My Phone

List the information that you would like nearby to help if you are suffering from overwhelming emotions.

Love You to the Moon Box

1. **This book, "Knowing Acts"**
2. **Essential oils**
3. **My power shirt**
4. **Photos**
5. **PowerBars**
6. **Colored pencils**
7. **Coloring book**
8. **My medicine**
9. **Totems** — *small gift turtle, small gift drawings, polished stones, beach pebble*

My Tote or Box

A tote or box can keep your calming items together and easier to access. List items you might include in your own box or tote that help you calm.

SEE PAGE 91

Support Others

We help ourselves by helping others. Jeanette LeBlanc says it well:

"Because in our pain we must find each other — mirror to mirror the grace of our shared humanity, the stunningly broken beauty of our shared grief.

And you can let your grief see my grief and let our tears mingle into some kind of healing alchemy, and you'll know what I know.

That we are never alone."

— Jeanette LeBlan

Break the Silence

I survived violent crime as a child and was silenced. The longer my secrets stayed inside me, the more they became overwhelming. Talking to therapists to slowly share my stories in a trusted setting was critical to my health and recovery. Gradually I was able to share my story with others and find myself open to listening to theirs.

I believe we all carry stories. Sharing our stories and breaking the silence can help us and others engage in healing. If you have ever felt silenced or are suffering from overwhelming emotions and do not have a counselor, please consider one. If you are not ready, interested, or able to share your story, that is your choice. Be gentle with yourself.

SEE PAGE 92

Seek Counseling or Therapy

I would have not have been able to find peace and healing without the help of professional therapists. *Knowing Acts* works best with support of a licensed therapist who can provide encouragement, insight, and hope through your healing process. If you are considering talking with a therapist and don't have one, use the space below to list those you might consider. If you aren't sure where to start, you can find therapists in your area through PsychologyToday.com/us/therapists.

Express My Feelings

Use these pages to keep track of overwhelming feelings and PTSD episodes. If you are working with a doctor or a therapist, you can bring this with you.

DATE

Express My Feelings

DATE

Where did The Pact originate?

Let me start by telling you a story. One day an eleven-year-old girl was hurt badly. She desperately wanted to run away. Everywhere she went, nightmares followed. She searched high and low to find ways to escape.

At age fifteen, when her friends were dancing at parties and putting on lipstick, she was hiding in dark corners of a library, afraid her demons would find her. She discovered a book of bright paintings and photographs. One picture made her gasp; it was the most beautiful waterfall she had ever seen. Water shimmered in the sunlight as it fell from a high cliff. A wild jungle surrounded her waterfall with lush green flora and bright red flowers. Sweet yellow birds flitted between the flowers. Zen-like cairns marked the path to its base where a silent reflecting pool beckoned her to come and bathe in the pool.

The girl was so excited she laughed out loud, which she had never before done in a library. Goose bumps traveled up and down her arms. She promised herself, in that moment, she would find that waterfall and live there for the rest of her life.

The girl's nightmares and night terrors continued for many years, and yet she always remembered the waterfall. She truly believed that if she bathed in that reflecting pool her demons would go away.

Many years passed, and the girl grew up. She found a pretty white sailboat, strong enough to carry her across the sea. On a windy day she left home to search for her secret waterfall.

As she sailed across vast oceans, scary storms followed. Her nightmares worsened. Several times she quit her journey, not trusting herself, believing it was too hard.

One day she met a very wise woman who had climbed near the top of the highest mountain in the world. The wise woman taught her how to make a book that would help chase away her demons and stand up to her fears. She made a pact with the wise woman and with herself. She said, ***"Whenever I feel really sad or scared I will open this book and follow its guidance—so that I can be strong, continue my journey, and live my dreams."***

She kept her promise and whenever she felt really sad or scared, when her demons came to haunt her, she pulled out her book. Completing the ACTS in her book calmed her wild mind and chased away her demons.

For five years she sailed across two oceans to a cluster of islands in French Polynesia. She sailed her pretty white boat to an alluring island with towering rock pillars and a multitude of birds and flowers like those from the library book. Rowing ashore, she searched far and wide until she finally found the cairns marking the path to her magical waterfall.

She had worked so hard using her book throughout her sail that by the time she found her waterfall and dove into its reflecting pool, her nightmares had already disappeared. She knew deep inside how to be at peace with herself.

Today that little girl has grown and wants to share with you how to make your own book. We all carry stories; some weigh us down. This book is about rising above the stories we carry to live fully and follow our dreams. The first step to make a pact, and the second is to ACT.

Detailed Instructions

Your first step is to ACT. Signing your name is simply a commitment to a healing path.

The Pact

I ______________________________

(sign your name)

will learn new ways to address overwhelming sadness, anger, & feelings of loss or despair, and grab this book

TO ACT

if I start to spiral down.

Page 9—THE PACT

Signing is an ACT of courage in an effort to enhance your journey. If through your journey you find better, nonviolent ways to reduce suffering from sadness, despair, and anger, that would be courageous. I put this Pact first in my book so I would always remember it. If you want to edit the pact, or use a name that's different from your birth name, yet meaningful to you—go for it. My real name is Heidi Love, and sometimes I just use the name Love.

You can celebrate your signing. This is a step toward addressing overwhelming emotions. Feel free to decorate your Pact, draw a frame around it, use colored pencils or markers in a way that shows joy and creativity for you. Even when you don't feel joyful, expressions of joy and happiness can help you move toward that direction. The next most important step is to try an exercise and continue to ACT.

Page 10—THE PRACTICE

During PTSD triggers, I felt totally overwhelmed, my self-esteem would plummet, and I was unable to ask for help. There were also times I felt unworthy of help. Having a PRACTICE or an automatic response of step-by-step ACTS was life saving. I made a PACT with myself that if I began to spiral down emotionally, I would open my book and ACT.

Page 10 lists the ACTS I used in an order that worked for me. Page 11 is a place for you to develop your own PRACTICE. You may want to leave this page blank to start. After you try several exercises in this workbook you can return to page 11 and list your ACTS in an order that works best for you.

Page 12—SAFETY PLAN

Safety can be an issue for anyone who has been affected by sexual or gender-based assault or domestic violence, or has had suicidal thoughts or overwhelming emotions. Concerns can include being safe from violence by others as well as yourself. Your Safety Plan can help you reduce your risk of future harm. There are great resources to help you create a safety plan. (See Resources, page 62.)

This is a place to add specific directions that will help keep you safe. I used it for emergency phone numbers of people in my support system. It reminded me of what to say to them. Before I had this book, I would typically call a friend and downplay how much trouble I was in. I used words like, "This isn't a big deal, but ..." or "I'm really fine, but ..." or "Don't worry about me, I just wanted you to know..." or my most common, "Just thinking of you. Call me back if you feel like it." I made the calls when my self-esteem was really low, and I wanted to disappear and not bother my friends. I minimized the urgency. What my friends heard was "Call me back if it's convenient." What I should have communicated is, "I'm in trouble; can you please help me get help!"

Page 14—PLAYLIST 1

This is my favorite ACT. Songs give me strength and power. When I sing along with Pink that I'm "F**kin' Perfect" it brings me to a better place. I feel like she's singing directly to me. I've made several playlists, long and short, a few that help me feel stronger, and others that calm and soothe.

Playlist 1 has lyrics that help me to feel stronger and loved. Playlist 2 is more instrumental and calming. Some of the selections also include sounds in nature.

When I started my very first playlist I asked several friends if they would find songs for me. My girlfriend Judy gave me the song "Stand by Me," and whenever I play it, I feel her standing with me. It's one of the best, longest lasting hugs I can imagine.

Now I give songs to others and sometimes they surprise me by making playlists on Spotify that I can access. I love to hear from readers and listen to their playlists. I have a friend, Hazel, who created a playlist. She used to play it to make the days brighter. Today she plays it when she's happy or sad, because she loves the songs and it reminds her of how courageous she is.

The goal is to choose songs that help bring your mood to a better, calmer place, not to make a list of your favorite songs. You can start this right away by choosing one song that helps to brighten your mood. I list several examples on page 14. You can listen to my playlists, Hazel's list, those from other readers, and share your own. Visit my blog Heidi-LoveAuthor.com/playlist for a link. And if you like any of the lists, please leave a ♥ on Spotify.

Page 16—FRAGRANCES & ESSENTIAL OILS

For centuries people have used the aromatic fragrances of essential oils to calm the body and mind. Putting a single drop on the palm of your hand or placing the vial close to your nose and smelling the fragrances can have an immediate effect on your focus. Some essential oils like bergamot and rose can have a calming effect; others like grapefruit oil may help to keep you present. You can Google "essential oils" or speak to someone in a health food store that carries them. You might choose to ask a therapist about whether this might help support your healing journey.

My therapist suggested I try these, so I went to my nearby health food store and spoke with a knowledgeable clerk. I tried several fragrances and landed on grapefruit, because its scent surprises me out of a downward emotional spiral. In an instant my mind shifts from thoughts of the past to the grapefruit scent in front of my nose. I chose orange and rose to soothe. I use these oils along with the breathing techniques that follow.

Page 18—BREATHE & RECITE MANTRAS

Deep breathing and paying attention to my breath help to focus my mind on the present moment, away from past hurts or future self-sabotaging thoughts. There are lots of stress-relieving breathing exercises, yoga, and Buddhist mantras to use. Feel free to copy mine, or use a computer search to find specific ones that speak to you. You can find free mindfulness exercises in Love's Resources, page 62.

Page 20—BE PRESENT

When I find myself overwhelmed with emotions, my mind races to remember bad experiences and imagine terrible futures. At times I feel detached as though my thoughts are separating from my body. I lose the power of being present. There are ways to help me refocus on the present and come back to my body by repeating aloud what day and year it is.

I also use all my senses to name what I am actually seeing, hearing, feeling, smelling and tasting around me. For example, in my bedroom I see black and white photos from Alaska, cream colored walls, a clock that shows 8:52, my phone, a bedspread with red flowers, and photos of my family. I try to just name what I see rather than remember where the Alaska photo was taken. I try not to think about what I must do at 8:52. I simply name what I see, hear, touch, smell, and taste. I breathe, stretch, and release overwhelming energy and try to be present in the NOW. I turn the page to the next ACT.

Page 22—FIND QUOTES

I love to find quotes that inspire me. If you Google inspirational quotes on any topic, you will find those that speak to you. Include them here.

Page 24—PHOTOS or SKETCHES

This is a place to glue or tape photos that lift you up. They can be of friends, family, pets, places, or possessions that bring you joy. If you take photos on a smart phone, you can print them online or at a local drugstore. If you prefer, sketch people or places, or write their names in a pleasant way. Only include those that are calming.

Page 26—CALMING THOUGHTS

In the classic movie *The Sound of Music*, Julie Andrews sings a song called "My Favorite Things." It starts out with the way she loves raindrops, kittens, packages with a surprise inside, and all of her "favorite things" that make her happy. It has been redone numerous times by artists like Sarah Vaughan, John Coltrane, Butterscotch, Ariana Grande, and John Legend.

This ACT is to write down things that lift your mood and bring you joy. They can be physical items like sneakers or cars, places like the ocean or Italy, memories from happy moments, friends, foods, or anything that makes you feel calm. Describe them in detail to help them come alive for you in pleasant ways.

Sometimes an item or person you love can create mixed emotions. A favorite pet may make you happy but her loss can make you sad. In this section, try only to include those items that are calming.

Page 28—GOOD TRAITS

Often others will see positive aspects of who we are that we may not see ourselves, especially during periods of overwhelming emotions. One of my coworkers once said to me, "I'm glad you're here; the cream always rises to the top." When I'm spiraling down I never think of myself this way. I write down quotes from friends, teachers, and colleagues who have complimented me so I can remember. When I read them, they help lift my self-esteem and give me added strength.

This is also a place you can add accomplishments. Have you ever created a piece of art you are proud of, did well in an athletic or school competition, helped a friend or family member, etc.? Write down some of the things you are good at in school, sports, friendships, at work, at home, or in life.

Page 30—NOURISHMENT

Many of us have comfort foods that may help to improve our mood.

like to drink iced tea and eat chocolate. One of my favorite chocolates is PowerBar because I imagine the strength its name brings me. I slowly hew each bite and savor the flavors and nourishment. I think about the ngredients it contains and how it was made.

once at tended a healing retreat with a Vietnamese monk named Thich Nhat Hanh. When we had meals, he suggested being present and grateful or each bite of food. The idea was to feel the food in your mouth to chew and taste slowly. By thinking of each ingredient the food is made from, and imagining how it was made and grown, it can increase our presence and gratitude for the food.

try to imagine the growing of plant-based ingredients like sugar cane, cocoa bean plants, or tea fields. I think about the sun and rain that nurtured the plants, how the wind spread the seeds, and the clouds that brought the wind and rain. I imagine the people who harvested the plants. I picture terraces in faraway lands and men and women harvesting tea. If you're not sure how some plants are grown you can do a computer search and look at images.

I also find that when I haven't nourished my body properly it impacts my mood. Often when I haven't had enough protein my mood and energy drop and my anxiety increases. I have a particular fondness for protein smoothies my stepdaughter, Hannah, makes with fresh vegetables and fruit. Eating healthy foods reminds me that I am nourishing my mind, body, and soul.

Sometimes recreational drugs and alcohol make us temporarily feel good, forget our troubles, avoid pain, or feel like we are in control. Yet painful emotions can be good by alerting us to unfinished work which may help our growth and well-being. While physician prescribed medicines are important to take as directed, recreational drugs and alcohol can make suffering from overwhelming emotions worse. I love red wine; however, it is not on my list here because when my emotions spiral down, wine depresses my mood and magnifies my reactions.

Page 32—INSPIRATION

People find inspiration in a variety of ways. Some use religion or philosophy, books or movies, people or natural elements. My dad was a Methodist minister and he loved to recite the Lord's Prayer. If you pray you can write a prayer here or lines of scripture. If there are other religious passages, Buddhist sayings, quotes, or acts of inspiration you like, place them here. I am calmed and inspired by the sea. I found art and poetry to remind me of the sea's beauty.

Page 34—A SENSE OF PLACE

Imagine a place you have been where you feel at peace with your surroundings. There is a marsh where I feel alive and loved. Describe your place as best and completely as you can. Use all of your senses: what does it look like, sound like, smell like .... Imagine feeling parts of it with your hands or feet. Use as many adjectives as you can to make it seem alive. Now close your eyes and bring that place to you.

Page 36—PUZZLES, COLORING, & GAMES

Fear can be a useful emotion to help you prepare for, or flee from, danger. Likewise, sadness and anger may be your body's way of reminding you of unresolved emotions to work through and heal. If you are suffering from overwhelming emotions, puzzles, games, and coloring can be meditative, a calm way to defuse them until you can seek help. I have a puzzle app on my iPad that I use. Doing a downloaded puzzle brings me relief quicker than focusing solely on medicine, music, and breathing. Mindfulness coloring books, especially those designed to reduce stress and panic attacks, are another creative way to bring calm.

Page 38—MEDITATION & MORE MANTRAS

Meditation can calm your mind and soul. There are many ways to meditate. If you have a preferred meditation, add it here. If not, or if you are ready to try a new one, you can look online or in your local library. See Love's Resources, page 62.

Initially, it was all I could do to just sit and breathe. I found I had to start with short periods. Although there seem to be many practitioners who like to practice for twenty minutes, it was difficult for me to sit for that long. I started with five minutes and increased as time went on or it fit my schedule. There are free applications, like "Insight Timer," to help with your timing and keep track of how many consecutive days you meditate.

The feeling that they are "doing it wrong" stops some people. I heard someone say once that it is very difficult to stop the thoughts; afterward I was able to release that judgment. What I have found most important is leaving judgment out. Our minds have difficulty keeping focused on one thing. Understanding that no one gets it "right" the first time, or even after months, is important. Thoughts will interfere. Once you find yourself "thinking," come back to your breath. Don't judge yourself. Just come back to the breath. The act of showing up and trying is perfect.

In addition to meditation I use Buddhist chants to calm me. The one I like best is a simple repetition of "om mani padme hum." Read about mantras and chants, and learn more about what they are and what they can do for you. Use this section to add your own chants and mantras.

Page 40—POWER CLOTHES & TOTEMS

My therapist, Susan Lord, once hiked to 24,000 feet on Mt. Everest with a team of scientists who were studying the effects of high altitude on the body. Her job was to record her breathing. It was a huge accomplishment. Afterwards she told me whenever she has to do something challenging she puts on the same hiking bra she wore climbing Mt. Everest. It makes her feel powerful. I have a shirt from the Broadway musical ***Rocky***, a fictional boxer who rose above being a street boxer to become world champion. My shirt is red with a Rocky illustration and the words "Love Wins." I wear it to feel brave. It helps to alter my mindset and give me power.

You can choose any type of clothing, something from a friend or relative, a piece you wore when you were doing a brave act, a shirt from a special place you visited, one with a quote on it that helps you to feel strong, or even a bracelet or armband that has meaning. In New England we have

"Life is Good" T-shirts that bring smiles to many owners. If you don't have anything similar, find, buy, or make something new. Or you can ask a friend for a gift.

Page 42—FRIENDS & CONTACTS

Developing a support system is an important part of staying safe and rising above trauma. Being part of someone else's support system can also improve your own healing. I have multiple people in my support system; when one is busy or having difficulties, another is likely available. I utilize their support in multiple ways including conversations of support, photos of joyful memories with them, songs, quotes, and totems they have gifted me. When I was at sea for long periods, I played the songs they recommended, like "Stand by Me," to bring them closer and feel as if we were together in community.

Page 44—PODCASTS

There are numerous podcasts I play when I start to spiral down.
One of my favorites is *Unbroken: Healing Through Storytelling* by Madeleine Black. She interviews ordinary people who have risen above major challenges and achieved the extraordinary (madeleineblack.co.uk/podcast). Take some time to list inspiring podcasts to play when you need more inspiration, courage, or joy in your life. There are also calming audio books. The application Audible has carefully selected playlists. Take some time to find and list inspiring and calming podcasts and audio books to play.

> *"It's not what happens to us that's important but what we do with what happens to us, and if we choose to, we can get past anything that happens to us in life."*
>
> — *Madeleine Black*

Page 46—STRETCH, DO YOGA, OR WALK

Exercise is amazing for mental and physical health. I like to do a variety of exercises including hiking, sailing, swimming, skiing, yoga, walking, and running. For my workbook I list exercises that are readily available to me. I can choose to do any or all of these. The idea is to find at least one exercise that you can do anywhere.

Page 48—DANCE

Dancing can release emotions. Merging mind, body, and soul can calm the chaos. You might twirl, sway, or twist, moving your whole body or just your head, or simply imagine how musical notes may swirl around you. Some find humming and singing provide additional release. The steps aren't important; just dance as if no one is watching. As for me, I start moving my head until I feel the music. If dancing calms you or helps you release emotion, write about specific movements here. For example, choose three songs or name a playlist and write down the steps you like to use.

Pages 50—PLAYLIST 2

Once I choose an exercise or dance (pages 46, 48), I select music. If I am going for a run, I take Playlist 1, my power songs. If I'm taking a walk or doing yoga stretches, I put on Playlist 2 with instrumental selections and nature sounds. If I choose a full yoga session I will start with a podcast, and then when I'm finished I often switch to Playlist 2. Choose calming songs and nature sounds to complete this page of your workbook.

Visit HeidiLoveAuthor.com/playlist for a free link to listen to my Spotify playlists. If you like any of them please consider clicking the hearts to like them. If you would like to create and share your own list you can name it Knowing Acts *your name* and include the link on my blog. Or simply share the name of a favorite song on my blog. It may even end up in the next edition. We are stronger together. You never know who you might inspire or where it might lead.

Page 52—EXAMPLES OF COURAGE

It is remarkable how many people have made extraordinary achievements in their lives after rising above major challenges. A few years ago, I was listening to a National Public Radio feature about an impoverished Nigerian girl who was deaf. She filled herself with courage, and in time became a university professor in the United States. I found her life so inspiring that I started a blog, LaughingAtTheSky.org.

Linda Kretzler
Photo: Kay Cottingham Robinson

I have had personal interviews with numerous people from all walks of life. For example, Linda Kretzler left an abusive situation to become an award-winning sky diver, breaking fourteen world records and raising millions for charity; Hibo Wardere left her war-torn homeland after a traumatic childhood to become a champion for children; Cecilia Aragon, Madeline Black, Winnie Li, Lizbeth Meredith, Ann Daniels, Amanda Gorman and other amazing women are on my blog. They have transcended trauma and brought incredible gifts to the world. Read their stories and mine on LaughingAtTheSky.org, and join the blog's conversation. Search for people who inspire you, and write their names on page 53.

One day you may inspire someone else, or perhaps you already are! As Dr. Hallward, Tufts psychiatrist, once said to me, *"Courage is contagious."*

Page 54—POETRY & SLAMS

Poetry in written, spoken, slammed, or rapped form can be very healing. My favorite SLAM poet is Amanda Gorman. She performs in powerful ways to inspire and bring meaning and tears of joy to me. Find poems, slams, and raps that inspire and transform your mood to one of joy and hope. You can also write and perform your own.

Page 56—HAIKU

I use haiku while I'm sailing, because if I'm far away from land my favorite communication device has a limit of 160 characters. I find it a calming way to be creative and to share my creativity with very few words. I use the ancient tradition of five syllables in the first line, seven syllables in the second line, and five syllables in the third line.

My dear friend Janet uses haiku to balance and calm her mind. She lives in Maine and often writes about what she sees in her home or through her window. I've included samples of her work.

You can use these spaces to create your own haiku, or create them in a separate book and copy your favorite calming haiku's here. Try the 5–7–5 style or try a contemporary haiku with one to four short lines, no strict syllable counts, just brief lines with asymmetry, i.e. short/medium/short/medium or medium/short/medium.

Read additional haikus and consider sharing yours by visiting HeidiLoveAuthor.com/haiku. We would love to hear from you.

Page 58—GRATITUDE

Trauma can make us hypervigilent and we look for danger. Gratitude helps us to reorient to a positive present.

Remind yourself of anything you might be grateful for. This can be specific friends or family members, pets, places, foods, personal items, or more. It can be huge, like the love I have for my son, or small like being able to feel my soft pillowcase. The top section is for long-lasting gratitude; the bottom should stay blank. The numbers are there to remind you to think of your present gratitudes in each moment you visit the page.

For a year while I was undergoing therapy, I often found myself triggered. Every night I would say five things that I felt that were positive that day. It often started with: I am safe in my bed, I can feel the softness of my pillowcase, ... and moved on from there. Even when it was hard to find gratitude, I could look around me and be grateful for air and water.

Page 60—BRAVE BOOKS

There are numerous books for mindfulness and inspiration. I've listed a few of my favorites here, and you can find more on my blog at LaughingAtTheSky.org. If you have a favorite book to share with others or one that might enhance the next edition of this book, please join our conversation on the blog.

Page 62—RESOURCES

The internet is full of wonderful resources: helplines, chats, free mindfulness and meditation exercises. Use this space to note your favorites.

Page 64—RITUALS

We each have our own ways to move toward calm. This space is for you to add more of your personal ACTS. I started my own ritual around making a warm cup of tea: feeling the warmth of my grandmother's teacup in my hand and remembering the comfort she brought to me, breathing in the aroma and letting it swirl around me, and slowly sipping the tea, letting the warmth fill me.

I made a second ritual out of caring for my house plants, moving from one to the next, pruning, watering, and observing. A Gestalt therapy coach told me that caring for something alive, such as a plant or pet, helps to bring meaning to some of her clients. A psychiatrist told me that some people use cold showers to release endorphins. There were also times I used physician-prescribed medicine so I included the ACT "Take 1 pill" in my original book. There are numerous healthy ways to seek calm. Add those that work for you, and make them into a healthy habit.

Page 66—BE CREATIVE

This is your book; these are your pages. Are there other ways that help you when your emotions spiral down? Use these spaces for your notes, ideas, doodles, drawings, or anything that might bring you peace. At the end of my action plan I simply added "Give yourself a hug" and "Be present and grateful in your life."

Complete Your Practice

As you fill in the blanks of your workbook, consider what works most effectively to improve your mood. Begin to determine the order that makes the most sense to you. Next, return to page 11, and fill in your own PRACTICE.

Set Up Your Phone

I use the notes section on my phone to hold a second copy of my PRACTICE, important phone and text information, reminders of my Spotify playlists, and special photo folders I have created. I'm rarely without my phone, so this information is near whenever I need it. If you have a smartphone you may want to add a folder with these items on it:

Use a Tote or Box

It's important to have your *Knowing Acts* easily accessible. I have a computer file on my phone. I also have my PRACTICE and a small pack of accessories (photos, essential oils, totems ...) in my car's glove box.

I have a special box with my actual *Knowing Acts* book and numerous accessories that I keep in my home or on my boat. My box includes my completed *Knowing Acts* workbook, essential oils, photos, PowerBars, totems (a small toy turtle a friend gave me and pebbles from my favorite beach), a stress-relieving coloring book and colored pencils, a T-shirt that says "Love Wins," and my iPad. These are items that keep me feeling safer.

You can use a canvas tote, handbag, shoebox, or plastic carrying case from the local general store. It is especially nice to gift yourself a special decorative box that you've personalized or infused with your own meaning. UNICEF market has beautiful handmade boxes, as do numerous art museums. Better yet, decorate your own! The important part is to have your healing materials easily accessible.

Support Others

We help ourselves by helping others. When you volunteer and help others, it doesn't take long to see that you are not alone. You have experiences and gifts to share and inspire. As you begin an ACT, you may find sharing it makes the ACT stronger and more powerful.

My friend Hazel was once very sad. I told her about a few of my ACTS and gifted her a song. She created her own playlist, sent it back to me on Spotify, and she now shares it with others. Simple ACTS of kindness can go a long way to help others while lifting ourselves.

COMING HOME

SINGULAR ACTS OF COMPASSION CAN
HAVE PROFOUND CONSEQUENCES.
YOU NEVER KNOW WHO YOU MIGHT INSPIRE
OR WHERE THE INSPIRATION MIGHT LEAD.

— Heidi Love

Break the Silence

Sharing our stories is an important part of full recovery, and also plays a role in reducing the culture of silence. I am a strong advocate for breaking the silence and speaking our truth. In the main body of *Knowing Acts,* however, I have purposely chosen to use terminology that is less triggering for readers who may be in crisis. For example,I wrote "Where did the Pact Originate" *(page 76, 77)* in story form. I used words like "violent crime" rather than provide specific details of the crime. While some survivor advocates may disagree with this approach, I believe it is my choice when and how to share my story. I honor all survivors as they make their own personal decisions if and when they want to share the stories they carry—it is their choice.

(Trigger Warning) I choose to be clear and open about my story here, with a warning attached. Like many around the world, I experienced repeated inappropriate sexual exposure throughout my childhood and young adulthood. The most severe was at age eleven, when I was raped by a friend's father. My mother realized what had happened and tried to strangle me until I lost consciousness. Three separate counselors surmised from Mother's letters that she had Borderline Personality Disorder and that her response was a result of a mental disorder, likely from her own childhood trauma. My visits to the emergency room, police interrogation, and court appearance added to my trauma.

Over the years I have learned ways to heal and make a full recovery. If you would like to know more about my story, and those of others who have risen above trauma, go to HeidiLoveAuthor.com.

Importantly, for anyone who has survived rape, sexual assault, incest, and/or domestic violence, my message is clear—it is not your fault.

With love,

Singular Acts of Compassion

I had a dream at age fifteen to run away or rather sail to the Bay of Virgins in French Polynesia. By age sixty I finally realized my dream. When I was afraid and lost hope on my journey, my book kept me feeling safer. I am sharing this book—*Knowing Acts*—with you. I am also writing a memoir about my sail, and about rising above the stories we carry and living our dreams. Here is an excerpt:

> *Like the apocryphal butterfly whose wings fluttered and ultimately caused a storm on the other side of the world, perhaps a singular act of violence in a small house in Pennsylvania, or anywhere in the world, can have profound consequences for generations across time and space. Might this be true for singular acts of compassion?*
>
> *A book of poems that my son Nico gave me rests on my nightstand. On its garnet cover an image of an ancient carpet, with an intricate weave, complements the beautiful binding. Its author, Rumi, was a thirteenth-century Sufi poet. A bookmark stands as a placeholder for one of many favorite lines: "The wound is the place where light enters you." How do we recognize the fullness of our wounds? How do we invite the light in to illuminate our world? How do we put our voices back into our bodies? How do we transcend our fear and live our dreams?*

Cultivating compassion for ourselves and others helps us rise above fear. I have another favorite saying: "*Singular acts of compassion can have profound consequences. You never know who you might inspire or where it might lead.*" When we share our truth we bring compassion to ourselves and begin to break down the culture of silence.

f you have a story you haven't fully shared, might it be time to break he silence, slowly, safely with someone you trust? If you aren't working vith a therapist who is truly helping you, you may want to consider if it s time to find one. Perhaps today you will offer a singular act of compas-ion to yourself or the world. Perhaps you will fly with iridescent cobalt-lue butterflies, flapping your wings and creating change in yourself nd the world.

IN THE HEART OF THE HARBOR

Please Share

If you find this book or any of the ACTS helpful, please let others know. If you have a friend in need or know of a therapist who works with those suffering from overwhelming emotions, please consider sharing.

If you would like to join our conversation, we would love to hear from you. Please visit HeidiLoveAuthor.com.

Meet the Author

Emerging from violent crime as a child, Heidi Love embarked on a five-year, 12,000-nautical mile odyssey to sail from Maine to French Polynesia. Raging storms and PTSD flashbacks at sea uncovered repressed memories and threatened her life, inspiring her to find a path toward greater healing. Heidi created Knowing Acts, her second book, to inspire courage seekers on their journeys of self discovery. You can find more about Heidi, her other books, and inspirational seekers of courage on her websites. *(she/her)*

HeidiLoveAuthor.com
LaughingAtTheSky.org

Meet the Artist

Linden O'Ryan is a Maine watercolorist creating artworks of imaginary landscapes of the heart. In her journey of healing, this work grew out of a meditative practice to move herself from struggle to grace, from sorrow to joy. These works have also offered support and connection to the well being of others. Her artworks range from magical and whimsical to reverent and inspirational. Her art is available for purchase on her website. *(she/her)*

lindenoryan.com

THE HONORING TIME —BRENNEN LOWE

YOU LEFT IN A RIBBON OF TRANSLUCENT LIGHT
AS I STOOD IN THE SHALLOWS OF THE SHADOWS OF LIFE
BUT YOU SENT ME GOLDEN LIGHT, WHICH I NOW WEAR
BELONGING STILL TO THE EARTH'S UNIVERSE OF LIFE
AS YOU WHISPER LOVE TO ME.
IN GRATITUDE, FOR MY LOVE OF YOU.

Streaming Joy — Linden O'Ryan

It Takes A Village

CONTRIBUTORS

Dr. Anne Hallward
Dr. Susan Manfull
Dennis Jud
Judy Trepal
Janet Clemons
Denise D'Amboise

SPECIAL THANKS TO:

Laughing at the Sky
Susan Lord, PhD
Wendy Hoge, LCSW

For Therapists & Psychiatrists

Thank you for the critical work you do. We recommend readers use this book with a licensed therapist, as well as a psychiatrist if needed, as a central part of their healing. Feedback from therapists and psychiatrists is important to the evolution of this book—we welcome yours. Please contact us directly at HeidiLove@HeidiLoveAuthor.com.

To order discounted books in bulk you can contact us at HeidiLove@HeidiLoveAuthor.com. Thanks!

I THINK A HERO IS ANY PERSON INTENT ON MAKING THIS A BETTER PLACE FOR ALL PEOPLE.

— *Maya Angelou*

AND JUST LIKE THAT
I BEGIN TO BELIEVE AGAIN

She Prays for Resurrection — *Amanda Gorman*

HIKING THROUGH COLOR

HEIDILOVEAUTHOR.COM

You Are Not Alone

If you are in immediate danger **CALL 911** or your local emergency service now.

If you are having thoughts of suicide or violence, don't know where to turn, or want to talk to someone, you can call someone you trust or:

- National Suicide Prevention
  800-273-8255
- RAINN Sexual Assault Hotline
  800-656-HOPE (4673)
- National Domestic Violence Hotline
  800-799-SAFE (7233)
- Womankind (Gender-based violence)
  888-888-7702
- The Trevor Project (LGBTQ+)
  866-488-7386

Add your contacts here:

____

____

____

____

CPSIA information can be obtained
at www.ICGtesting.com
Printed in the USA
BVHW092124241021
619685BV00003B/11